100 Farm Words

Have fun completing this sticker activity book.

Use your pens and pencils to color
the pictures. Where there is a missing
sticker, you will see an empty shape. Search
your sticker pages to find the missing sticker.

Then press out the cards at the back of the
book and use them to play a memory game!

make
believe
ideas

Busy farm

Point to the things that are red and brown.

trough

pig

tail

barn

cow

sheepdog

hay bale

sheep

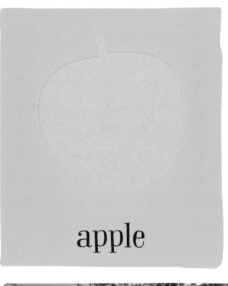

apple

crops

wheat

orchard

Draw a face on the scarecrow.

scarecrow

saddle

horse

By the pond

Can you find the animal that goes ribbit?

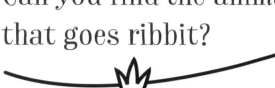
boots

duck

pond

lily pad

fish

Ribbit!

frog

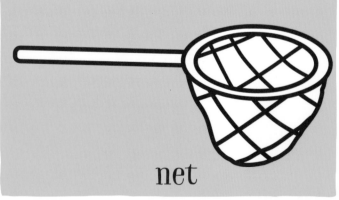
net

dragonfly

gate

Point to the animals that can fly.

goose

Swish!

Swish!

windmill

rabbit

beehive

Buzz!

bee

5

In the barn

How many of these animals have four legs?

horseshoe

straw

mouse

donkey

turkey

cat

whiskers

owl

chicken

rooster

llama

alpaca

Which bird wakes up early?

goats

bucket

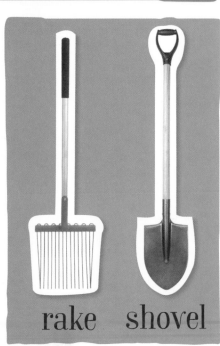

rake   shovel

7

Time to work

What do you pour on your cereal?

hat

farmer

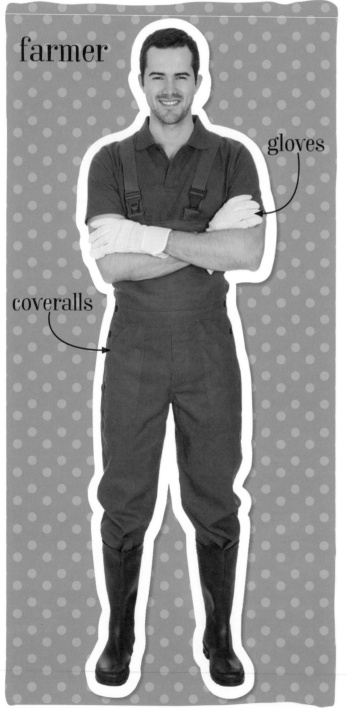

gloves

coveralls

herding

harvesting

milking

milk

milk jug

sheepshearing

wool

hat

Can you name the animals in the herd?

fruit picking

jelly

Baby animals

Which baby animal has hatched from its egg?

duckling

calf

lamb

hoof
kid

cria

paw
puppy

kitten

cygnet

goslings

eggshell

chick

piglet

Find the baby animal that has a fluffy tail.

ear

rabbit kitten

mane

foal

Farm food

How many different orange foods do you see?

pepper

pumpkins

potatoes

cauliflower

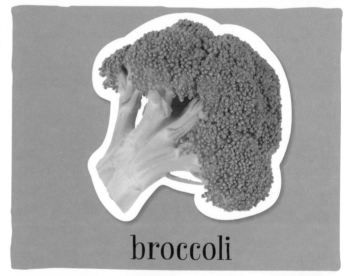

broccoli

peas

strawberries

tomato

eggs

bread

sweet corn

What is your favorite food?

carrots

cheese

berries

Things that go

Can you find the red mower?

wheelbarrow

tire

mower

light

plow

crop sprayer

steering wheel

compact tractor

ATV

combine harvester

wagon

baler

tractor

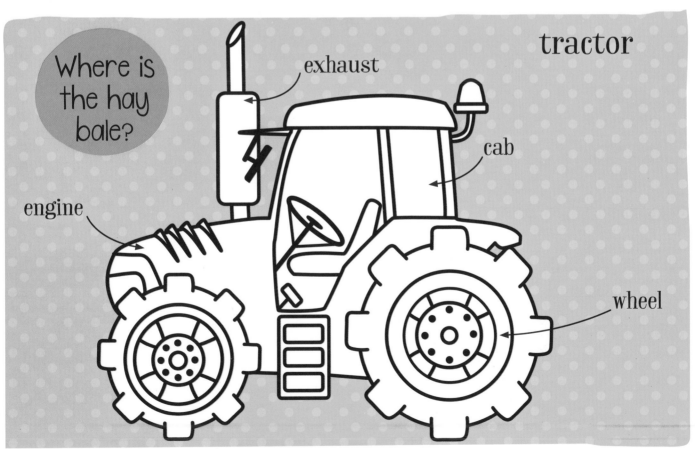

Where is the hay bale?

exhaust

cab

engine

wheel

Noisy animals

Can you make these animal sounds?

Cock-a-doodle-doo!

Baa! Baa!

Neigh! Neigh!

Meow!

Oink! Oink!

Color the noisy rooster!

Moo!

Woof! Woof!

16

Farmyard friends!

tractor

tractor

piglet

piglet

scarecrow

scarecrow

cow

duck

duck

puppy

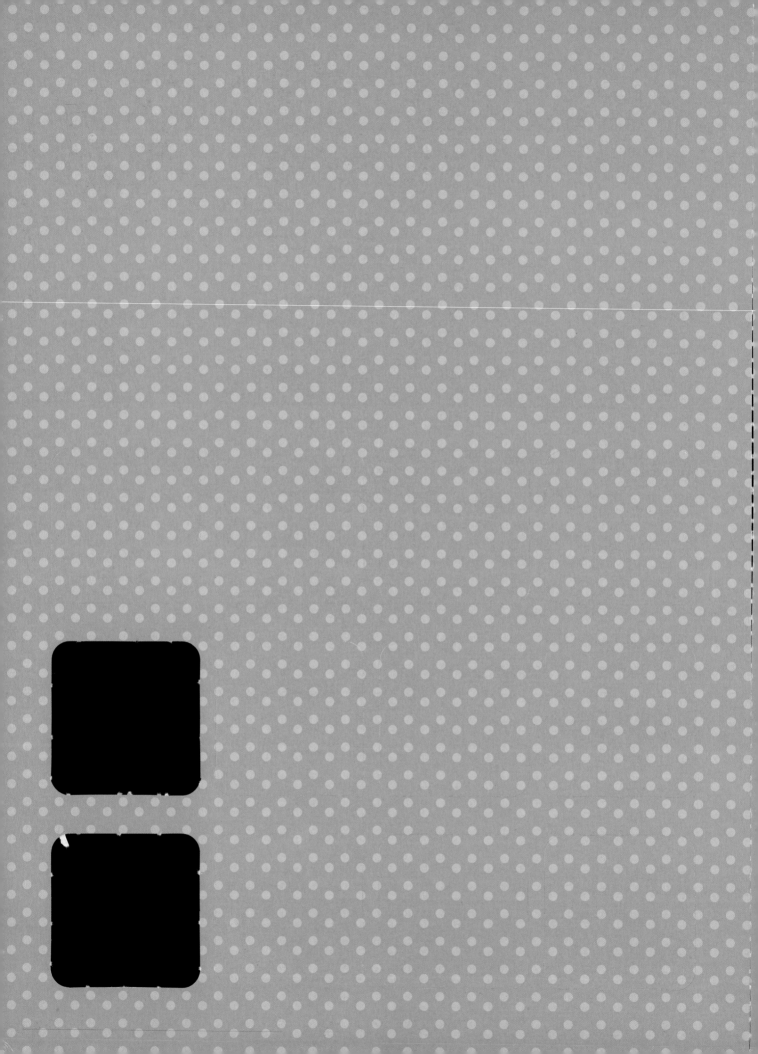

 apple
 apple
 bucket
 bucket

 llama
 llama
 chicken
 chicken

 mouse
 mouse
 duckling
 duckling

 barn
 barn
 foal
 foal

 kid
 kid
 sheep
 sheep

es 2-3

Pages 4-5

Pages 6-7

Pages 8-9

Pages 10-11

Pages 12-13

Pages 14-15

Page 16

Extra stickers